The
Old Hogan

Published By
Old Hogan Publishing Company
7887 N. LaCholla Blvd. #2131
P.O. Box 91978
Tucson, Arizona 85752-1978

Other Books by Margaret Kahn Garaway
Dezbah and the Dancing Tumbleweeds
Ashkii and His Grandfather
The Old Hogan Coloring Book
The Teddy Bear Number Book
in English and Spanish

8th Printing 1995   Copyright © 1993 by Margaret Kahn Garaway

Library of Congress Catalog Card Number

ISBN 0-9638851-0-3

Printed by Sahuaro Press, Ltd., 700 North Stone Avenue, Tucson, Arizona 85705

For my grandchildren: Oak, Sarah Ann, Heather Linn, Isaac Jacob, Shana Joy, Hope Ann, Anna Grace, Peter Douglas, Kenny and Amy and to all the Navajo students I taught over the past years.

The
Old Hogan

by Margaret Kahn Garaway
Illustrated by Andrew Emerson Bia

The hogan is more than just a house to the Navajo people. It is mother earth nurturing the family. The family is fed, sheltered and cared for within her walls; taught desired behavior, customs and traditions of the Navajo people (the Diné). That is why the hogan (hōghän bi aadii) is referred to as a female.

The old Navajo hogan stands alone amid the sand and sage brush of the desert. She feels the spring wind whip the sand around her gentle curves. She feels the tumbleweeds swirl and bounce against her.

The old hogan, for that is what the family lovingly calls her, does not mind the roar and fury of the desert sand storm. Old Grandfather built her well. He had packed the red mud so thick around the cedar log frame that it protects her from the wind, the rain, and the snow. The mud roof keeps her warm in the winter and cool in the summer. The old hogan has been happy and content all these years.

But, tonight, she is not happy. The old hogan cannot believe what is happening. Old Grandfather's grandchildren are skipping around the old oil drum stove. They are chanting, "We're going to move, we're going to move. We're going to live in a real house,

a real house,

A REAL HOUSE!"

"What is a real house?" wonders the old hogan. "Am I not a real house?" she wants to shout.

The family is very excited. They will be living in a six room house instead of a one room hogan. They will have a bathroom instead of an outhouse. They will have running water instead of barrels of water hauled from the well. And they will have electric lights, not lanterns. They talk of many new things the hogan has never heard of.

"The family does not love me anymore," thinks the old hogan and feels very sorry for herself. As the family sleeps she recalls all the wonderful things that have made her happy these many years.

How she loves to be blessed by the rising sun each morning. Grandfather has faced her doorway properly toward the east as all Navajo hogans should face.

She loves to wake up to the crackling sound of the piñion and juniper wood burning in the old stove. She loves to smell the smoke rising out of the hole in the middle of her mud roof.

She loves to smell the coffee perking in the morning and the mutton stew and fry bread cooking for the evening meal.

She loves to hear the sound of the animals stirring in the sheep-pen. She loves to hear the tinkle of the bells on the lead sheep and goat as they graze nearby.

She loves to look beautiful with the sheepskins lying upon her earthen floor and the hand woven rugs hanging upon the wall.

She loves to hear the teasing and laughter of the family when they gather together in the evening.

She loves to hear the Coyote stories old Grandfather tells his grandchildren after the first snow fall and all through the winter.

She loves, best of all, the ceremonies held inside her. Family and friends crowd into every inch of the old hogan to take part in the ceremonies. Ceremonies to welcome the first laughter of the new baby. Ceremonies to celebrate the coming of age of the girls in the family. Ceremonies to honor a marriage in the family. And, ceremonies to heal the sick.

Most of all, she loves to hear the chanting of the medicine men and the music of their sacred rattles.

These thoughts only make the old hogan feel sadder. "What is to become of me? Where will the new house be? Will I see the family anymore?" The old hogan is full of questions.

Suddenly, one morning the old hogan's world of peace and quiet is shattered. Men drive up in pickups and unload strange things not far from the hogan. They set up surveying instruments to lay out where the housing project is going to be built.

The children hear the commotion outside and jump out from under their covers. With a shout they rush to the door to see what is going on. The old hogan soon finds out what is happening. All the children can talk about during breakfast is the new housing project.

"So this is where their house is going to be," the old hogan thinks. She wishes she could tell the men to go away. But she feels helpless.

Soon all kinds of trucks drive up. The men unload wood, brick, pipes, wire, and many different things needed to build houses. The big tractors make lots of noise when they level the earth for the foundations.

The heavy concrete trucks ring their bells all day long as they pour the concrete. Each day it grows noisier and noisier with the pounding of hammers and the buzzing of saws. She does not like the noise.

The old hogan believes her world is coming to an end. No one in the family talks about her anymore. Will they forget her? Will the family leave her standing empty and cold? Will one of the big trucks knock her down and crush her? She is very worried.

Finally the day comes for the family to pack their possessions. The old hogan thinks she will not look pretty anymore as they remove the rugs from the wall. She will miss the rugs. She will miss the colorful clothes that hang upon the nails. She will miss the children's toys scattered upon the floor. She will miss the animals that come in out of the winter cold. She will miss lots and lots of things.

It is the last night the family will be living in the old hogan. They are having fry bread and mutton stew for dinner.

"Will I ever smell that delicious aroma of fry bread and mutton stew and feel the warmth of the stove again?" wonders the old hogan.

If the old hogan could cry there would be a pool of tears on the earthen floor. She wants to shout, "Don't leave me, don't leave me!"

The next morning the family moves out leaving only the old stove and some sheepskins on the floor. They are not aware that they have also left behind a hogan with a broken heart.

The new house is not far from the old hogan. She sees the children she loves so much playing outside. She wishes she could call out to them to play inside her. The old hogan wants to hear their laughter again. She feels forlorn and forsaken as she watches the family go in and out of their new house.

It seems, to the old hogan, that it has been a long time since the family has lived in her. Suddenly, one day her door is flung wide open. The family enters carrying arm loads of wood for the fire. Once more sounds of joy and laughter fill the old hogan as the family cooks fry bread and mutton stew.

The old hogan cannot believe what is happening! The family is getting ready for a ceremony. Old Grandfather's granddaughter is going to be married. She hears the family say, "*Houses* are not for ceremonies. *Hogans* are for ceremonies."

Now the old hogan knows that the family still loves her — that she is very important to them — that they are not going to abandon her. She will be part of all the ceremonies she so dearly loves. Her worry and sadness of the last few months leave her. If she had feet she would jump to the sky!

The old hogan is ready to enjoy the marriage ceremony. Friends and family gather inside. The bride and the groom wear their traditional Navajo clothes. They sit upon a beautiful hand woven Navajo rug. Many guests stand up and speak. They wish the couple a good and happy life together. After the last person speaks the bride and groom feed each other the corn mush which is inside the wedding basket. Now they are married. The guests then share the corn mush. There is much happiness and excitement while everyone partakes in the wedding feast.

After everyone leaves it is quiet and warm inside the old hogan. She gives a happy sigh. The old hogan knows she has her own special place in the life of the family.

Letters to the Author

*I am writing to inform you that I will be utilizing your book (*The Old Hogan*) in an elementary school at all grade levels. . . The book teaches the values and beliefs of the Navajo people. I am a Navajo. I felt good after I read this book. . .*

Anna Mae Jim, October '93, N.A.U. Flagstaff, Arizona

The Old Hogan, *by Margaret Kahn Garaway, is that unique blend of fact and fancy that informs and entertains at the same time. A modern-day fairy tale placed in the Southwest, the story is told through the thoughts of the traditional Navajo home, a hogan. The hogan lives her past happiness when she learns that her family will soon move to a modern home.*

It paints a picture of a culture that is ever-evolving and ever-changing, the Navajo Indians of the Southwest. The author, while not Navajo has obviously gained insight into some of the Navajo values during her many years teaching on a Navajo Reservation.

Jimmie Bevill, Youth Service, June '88,
Flagstaff City, Arizona - Coconino County Public Library

It is with pleasure that I write this letter of congratulations on your children's story, The Old Hogan. . .*(The book) will provide a glimpse of authentic Navajo culture to all who read it. The reader is able to join in a culture moving from a traditional experience to a modern one. The book is enjoyable for both young and old. Children will learn the art of telling a story from a different perspective than their own. Your book is an excellent teaching guide for this skill.*

Mary Ann Hunter, Supt. of Schools. February '90, Chinle, Arizona

The Old Hogan is a lucid and an exceptional description of change's challenge to tradition. An "early" reader is given an interesting introduction of change's challenge to Navajo family life. It's not a local problem but a universal one.

Bob & Roz R. Lennox, Massachusetts
Two retired New York teachers

I really liked The Old Hogan because she has so many feelings that a real person would have.
Your friend, Lucy
I really liked The Old Hogan. I liked the part when they came in for the celebration. And I liked the way you gave the hogan characteristics.

Sincerely, David
Sampling from Mrs. Kuyendall's 3rd grade class,
Flagstaff, Arizona

Your book is perfect. Absolutely perfect! One can tell it was written by a person who knows children and the Indian culture. It is sensitive, informative and the vocabulary and sentence length is appropriate to the child. BRAVO! Also you chose a fine artist.

Solveig Leslie, Los Angeles, California
Artist and former teacher

Yesterday I tried The Old Hogan on my 8 year old granddaughter. She read and I read and it met with her approval as well as mine. She should know being the daughter of a librarian and exposed to books from the cradle on.

Lucy Kolkin, New York City grandma